Garfield

Goes Wild

JIM DAVIS

RAVETTE BOOKS

This edition first published by
Ravette Books Limited 1988
Reprinted 1989

Printed in Great Britain
for Ravette Books Limited,
3 Glenside Estate, Star Road, Partridge Green,
Horsham, West Sussex RH13 8RA
by The Guernsey Press Company Limited,
Guernsey, Channel Islands
and bound by
WBC Bookbinders Limited,
Maesteg, Mid Glamorgan.

ISBN 1 85304 072 X

Garfield

Garfield is an animal at heart. When in the wilds of suburbia he reverts to his primal self, stalking his prey with buttered bread in hand. Mustering all the skills at his disposal; cunning, resourcefulness and a good deal of imagination; he transforms into the night stalker, lurking in shadows, invisible to his adversaries he seeks out his target and strikes with animal ferocity and another lasagna bites the dust!

GARFIELD

FROM DEEP WITHIN GARFIELD'S WORST FEARS IT... CAME!

SEE! THE MONDAY THAT WOULDN'T DIE!

Z

SEE! THE ATTACK OF THE INCREDIBLE SLOBBER MONSTER!

SEE! THE INTERMINABLE VISIT OF THE CUTEST KITTEN ON EARTH!

ARRRGH!

SEE! THE CAN OPENER THAT WOULDN'T WORK!

UNNGH!

TOINK TOINK TOINK

WAKE UP, GARFIELD. WANNA GO TO A MOVIE?

IT'S NOT VIOLENT, IS IT?

© 1986 United Feature Syndicate, Inc.

IT'S CALLED "SLIME PIT ZOMBIE CHAIN SAW MASSACRE"

AS LONG AS THERE ARE NO MONDAYS IN IT

JIM DAVIS 8-3

BEEP BEEP BIP BOOP

HELLO? LOST AND FOUND? TAKE THIS DOWN. "MISSING: MY TWO PRECIOUS PETS ANSWERING TO THE NAMES 'GARFIELD' AND 'ODIE'. WHEN FOUND, CONTACT JON ARBUCKLE, 711 MAPLE STREET. LARGE REWARD. REPEAT, LARGE REWARD."

THAT "LARGE REWARD" BIT WILL HAVE EVERYBODY LOOKING

CLICK

© 1986 United Feature Syndicate, Inc.

THE NEXT DAY...

AH! THERE'S MY AD. JON BOY, YOU THOUGHT OF EVERYTHING

DING DONG ♫

I WONDER WHO THAT COULD BE?

JIM DAVIS 8-31

WHOA, SIMBA! ER I MEAN, ODIE

I FOUND GARFIELD AND ODIE, MITHTER

MAYBE I SHOULD HAVE BEEN MORE SPECIFIC

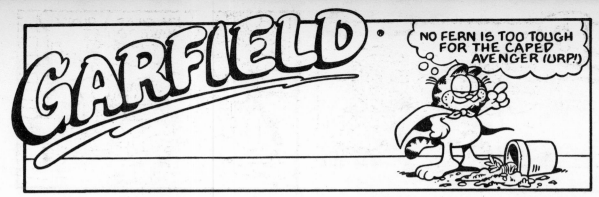

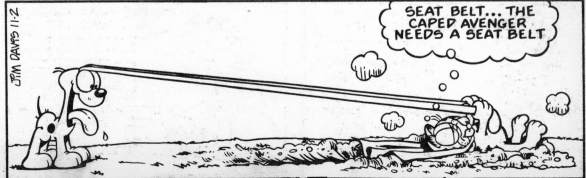

© 1986 United Feature Syndicate, Inc.

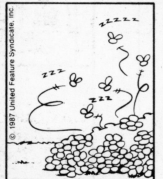

IT WAS HIGH NOON WHEN THE STRANGER RODE INTO TOWN

4-27

JIM DAVIS

NOW COMES MY FAVORITE PART...

© 1987 United Feature Syndicate, Inc.

HE HITCHED UP HIS HORSE AND AMBLED INTO THE SALOON

I AM HUNGRY

4-28

THEREFORE I AM

© 1987 United Feature Syndicate, Inc.

RATIONALIZING ANOTHER BOUT WITH GLUTTONY, GARFIELD

I DON'T DISCUSS PHILOSOPHY WITH PEA BRAINS

JIM DAVIS

I'VE ONLY BEEN ON THIS DIET FOR TWO DAYS AND I FEEL THINNER ALREADY

© 1987 United Feature Syndicate, Inc.

IT MUST BE A DELAYED REFLECTION

JIM DAVIS 5-15

FAT'S A FUNNY THING, YOU NEVER LOSE IT FROM THE RIGHT PLACES

© 1987 United Feature Syndicate, Inc.

FAT HAS A SICK SENSE OF HUMOR

JIM DAVIS 5-16

GARFIELD! WHAT ARE YOU DOING?!

JIM DAVIS 5-29

I'M UNRAVELING YOUR DENTAL FLOSS

© 1987 United Feature Syndicate, Inc.

I HATE THAT!

OH, VERY WELL. TOMORROW WE'LL DO SOMETHING YOU LIKE

HERE YOU GO, GARFIELD!

JIM DAVIS 5-30

CRUNCH!

© 1987 United Feature Syndicate, Inc.

IT DOESN'T HAVE MUCH OF A SENSE OF HUMOR, DOES IT?

JIM DAVIS 5-31

GARFIELD

CRUNCH

YAWN

PUNT!

© 1987 United Feature Syndicate, Inc.

YAWN. I HAD THE MOST WONDERFUL DREAM LAST NIGHT

JIM DAVIS

6-14

WHUMP!

© 1987 United Feature Syndicate, Inc.

HAPPY BIRTHDAY, GARFIELD!!

THAT SURE IS A LOT OF CANDLES

OH WELL, I SHOULD BE HAPPY TO HAVE A BIRTHDAY, I GUESS

FFFFF

AS OPPOSED TO THE ALTERNATIVE

JIM DAVIS 6-19

YUP

I'M NINE YEARS OLD ALL RIGHT

ACCORDING TO THE RINGS UNDER MY EYES

JIM DAVIS 6-20

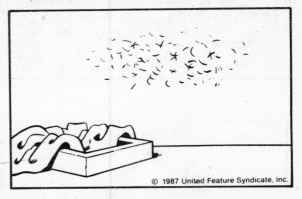

© 1987 United Feature Syndicate, Inc.

6-21

JIM DAVIS

GARFIELD

NO SOLICITING
ATTACK CAT
ON DUTY

OKAY, ODIE, NOW FOR A LESSON IN HOME PLUMBING

ALL THE WATER LINES IN THIS HOUSE ARE CONNECTED

© 1987 United Feature Syndicate, Inc

THUSLY, IF I TURN THE HOT WATER ON HERE, THERE WILL NO LONGER BE HOT WATER IN JON'S SHOWER

OBSERVE

JIM DAVIS 7-5

YEOWWW!

SHHH

GET OFF THAT SINK!

AIN'T SCIENCE GREAT?

GARFIELD

THIS COULD BE ANY REFRIGERATOR, MAYBE YOURS

DEEP WITHIN THE FROZEN WASTES IT LURKS

© 1987 United Feature Syndicate, Inc.

ANCIENT MAYONNAISE, FOSSILIZED CABBAGE, SLOWLY MUTATING OVER UNTOLD EONS, GRADUALLY ACHIEVING CONSCIOUSNESS...

UNTIL THAT TERRIBLE DAY WHEN IT IS UNLEASHED UPON AN UNSUSPECTING WORLD

THE COLESLAW THAT TIME FORGOT! AYIEEE!

JIM DAVIS 7-19

CUTE, GARFIELD. NOW FINISH CLEANING OUT THE REFRIGERATOR

QUIET, FOOL! YOU'LL AWAKEN THE SLEEPING SPUDS FROM THE PLANET FUNGUS

GARFIELD®

3 PIES for $1.00

HELLO, PLANTS

OH NO! SHOO! SCAT!

WELL, LET'S SEE WHAT'S ON THE MENU TODAY

MRS. BROWN! THERE'S A CAT OUT HERE!

I THINK I'LL START WITH A SALAD

NOOO!

RUN, HAROLD! RUN!

GLOMP

HAROOLD! HE GOT HAROLD!

BURP

OH, RALPH! WHAT WILL WE DO?!

STAY CALM, TAMMY. I'LL JUMP OFF THE SILL AND RUN FOR HELP!

© 1987 United Feature Syndicate, Inc

NOW FOR DESSERT

HURRY, RALPH! HURRY!

I THINK I BROKE SOMETHING!

JIM DAVIS 8-2

TAP
TAP
TAP

COOKIES

JIM DAVIS 8-5

© 1987 United Feature Syndicate, Inc.

WELL, WELL, WELL, AND JUST HOW DID YOU GET IN THERE?

WOULD YOU BELIEVE HOURS AND HOURS OF CAREFUL PLANNING?

GET UP, GARFIELD. BREAKFAST IS THE MOST IMPORTANT MEAL OF THE DAY, YOU KNOW

GARFIELD

YOU'RE QUITE RIGHT, JON. I COULDN'T AGREE WITH YOU MORE

GARFIELD

© 1987 United Feature Syndicate, Inc.

NOW, BE A GOOD BOY AND BRING IT BACK AT NOON

GARFIELD

JIM DAVIS

8-6

YOU KNOW, GARFIELD, LIFE IS LIKE A BOWL OF CHERRIES

© 1987 United Feature Syndicate, Inc.

8-7

LET DOWN YOUR GUARD, AND IT'LL GET YOU

YOU'RE GOING TO PAY FOR THIS ONE

HEY, GARFIELD, THEY'RE DEVELOPING COMPUTERS WITH ARTIFICIAL INTELLIGENCE

BIG DEAL

© 1987 United Feature Syndicate, Inc.

I'LL BE IMPRESSED WHEN THEY INVENT ARTIFICIAL CUNNING

JIM DAVIS

8-8

A selection of Garfield books published by Ravette

Garfield Landscapes

Garfield The All-Round Sports Star	£2.95
Garfield The Irresistible	£2.95
Garfield On Vacation	£2.95
Garfield Weighs In	£2.95
Garfield I Hate Monday	£2.95
Garfield Special Delivery	£2.95
Garfield Another Serve	£2.95
Garfield Wraps It Up	£2.95
Garfield This Is Your Life	£2.95
Garfield Sheer Genius	£2.95
Garfield The Incurable Romantic	£2.95

Garfield Pocket-books

No. 1	Garfield The Great Lover	£1.95
No. 2	Garfield Why Do You Hate Mondays?	£1.95
No. 3	Garfield Does Pooky Need You?	£1.95
No. 4	Garfield Admit It, Odie's OK!	£1.95
No. 5	Garfield Two's Company	£1.95
No. 6	Garfield What's Cooking?	£1.95
No. 7	Garfield Who's Talking?	£1.95
No. 8	Garfield Strikes Again	£1.95
No. 9	Garfield Here's Looking At You	£1.95
No. 10	Garfield We Love You Too	£1.95
No. 11	Garfield Here We Go Again	£1.95
No. 12	Garfield Life and Lasagne	£1.95
No. 13	Garfield In The Pink	£1.95
No. 14	Garfield Just Good Friends	£1.95
No. 15	Garfield Plays It Again	£1.95
No. 16	Garfield Flying High	£1.95
No. 17	Garfield On Top Of The World	£1.95
No. 18	Garfield Happy Landings	£1.95

Garfield TV Specials

Here Comes Garfield	£2.95
Garfield On The Town	£2.95
Garfield In The Rough	£2.95
Garfield In Disguise	£2.95
Garfield In Paradise	£2.95
Garfield Goes To Hollywood	£2.95
A Garfield Christmas	£2.95
The Second Garfield Treasury	£5.95
The Third Garfield Treasury	£5.95
The Fourth Garfield Treasury	£5.95
Garfield A Weekend Away	£4.95
Garfield How to Party	£3.95

All these books are available at your local bookshop or newsagent, or can be ordered direct from the publisher. Just tick the titles you require and fill in the form below. Prices and availability subject to change without notice.

Ravette Books Limited, 3 Glenside Estate, Star Road, Partridge Green, Horsham, West Sussex RH13 8RA

Please send a cheque or postal order, and allow the following for postage and packing. UK: Pocket-books – 45p for up to two books and 15p for each additional book. Landscape Series and TV Specials – 45p for one book plus 15p for each additional book. Treasuries, How to Party and A Weekend Away – 75p for each book.

Name...

Address...

....